THE CHIEF'S BRIDE

AN AFRICAN TALE

Written by Jenny Powell
Illustrated by Adrienne Kennaway

WAYLAND

The Chief's Bride can be used during Shared or Guided Reading sessions with individuals or small groups of children. It can also be performed by the class with named parts given to individual children and the rest of the class playing the parts of the extra villagers, the washer-women and the trees.

This play is a valuable tool for use in the Year 4 Literacy unit 3 'Stories from other Cultures' or within unit 5 about 'Plays'.

Sets and props

Creating the sets and finding the props can be just as much fun as putting on the performance! You could tape together some white paper to make some backdrops that you then paint to create the sets; you would need a backdrop for a village house, the road that the daughters travel along, the forest and river and the Chief's house.

You can perform the play without having to find lots of different props. For example, furniture for the two houses could be your classroom tables and chairs. You will need some trees to represent a thick forest – these could be made from long wrapping paper tubes and strips of green crêpe paper. You will also need some clothes for washer-women to wash – think about the sort of clothes they would be washing, such as Zimbabwean prints and other African clothing. The food Daya gives on her journey could be some plastic food or just something wrapped in a cloth to represent food.

Staging

There is no need to put on a huge production. All you need is a large enough space for a stage and room for an audience. If you have access to an outside space and the weather is good, you can even put on the play in the open air! This would be a fantastic setting for the journey that Maiba and Daya make from their village to the Chief's village.

Costumes

You'll need to think about the traditional dress worn in Zimbabwe for your costumes. Traditionally, Zimbabwean women wear beautiful big beads and ornaments. The central part of the male clothing is the 'breastplate' (or Iporiyana), which is a large piece of animal skin worn around the neck. You could design and make your own Iporiyana. The animals Maiba and Daya meet on their journies could be represented by puppets that you have made in class.

HAVE FUN PUTTING ON YOUR PLAY!
Go to www.waylandbooks.co.uk for more ideas.

Introduction

The play is based on the tale *The Story of Five Heads* by George McCall, told in his book *Kaffir Folk-lore*, published in 1886, and retells a Zimbabwean folktale. The tale was originally told by people living amongst the ruins of what was once the capital city of the Kingdom of Zimbabwe. Despite being a nineteenth-century folktale, the story's moral that kindness and goodness will always be rewarded still rings true today.

The characters in the play

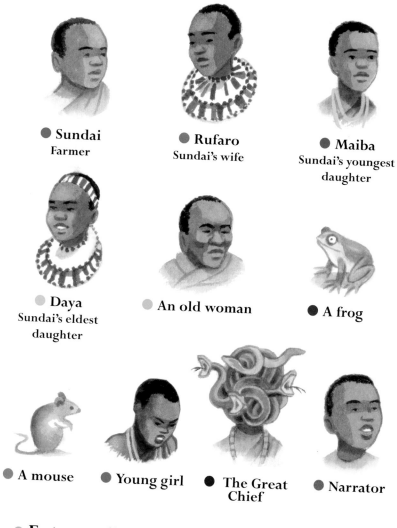

Sundai
Farmer

Rufaro
Sundai's wife

Maiba
Sundai's youngest
daughter

Daya
Sundai's eldest
daughter

An old woman

A frog

A mouse

Young girl

**The Great
Chief**

Narrator

Extras: *villagers, the bridal party, washer-women,
the wind and the trees.*

SCENE 1

CHARACTERS IN THIS SCENE:
- Narrator ● Sundai ● Rufaro ● Maiba
- Daya ● Extras – Villagers

Sundai is sitting down to eat breakfast as the sun rises in the village. Maiba and Daya enter the hut to greet their father. Villagers are listening in the doorway.

● **Sundai:** Good morning, Maiba. Good morning, Daya. I need to talk to you both about something very important.

●● **Maiba and Daya:** Yes, Father. What is it?

● **Sundai:** Yesterday, I travelled to the village beyond the river. I spoke with the villagers there and they say that the Great Chief is looking for a wife. Your mother and I think one of you should go to the Great Chief.

● **Maiba:** (*forcefully*) Father, it **must** be me who goes to the Great Chief. I want to be admired and respected across the land. I will surely be so if I am the wife of a Great Chief.

● **Villagers:** (*whispering*) Maiba's a proud young girl. Maybe the Great Chief won't want such a proud wife?

Narrator: Sundai and Rufaro do not want to listen to the gossip of the villagers. They love their daughter and agree Maiba should go to the Great Chief.

● **Rufaro:** (*excitedly*) You should go soon, Maiba. No time must be lost!

● **Sundai:** (*nodding*) Indeed, you shall go tomorrow.

Maiba smiles smugly to herself.

● **Narrator:** Maiba knows that as the wife of the Great Chief she will be rich beyond her wildest dreams.

● **Sundai:** I will gather a large bridal party to escort you. The Great Chief will be most impressed.

● **Maiba:** (*angrily*) No, Father, I do not want anyone to come with me. I will go alone.

● **Daya:** (*gasps and covers her mouth with her hand*) How can you say such a thing, Maiba? You know that you must have a bridal party. It is the custom in our village.

● **Rufaro:** I agree. Don't be foolish, Maiba, you must have a bridal party!

● **Maiba:** (*proudly*) I am not foolish, Mother, and I will have my way. I shall go alone.

A villager: (*whispering to the other* **villagers**) What is Maiba thinking? Surely the Chief won't accept her as his wife without a bridal party?

Narrator: Sundai knows his daughter is strong-minded and will not be persuaded.

Pause whilst **Sundai** *thinks about what to do.*
At last he speaks.

Sundai: (*nodding at his daughter*) Very well, my daughter, you may do as you wish.

SCENE 2

CHARACTERS IN THIS SCENE:

- Narrator ● Maiba ● A mouse ● A frog
- An old woman ● Extras – Villagers

Maiba sets off along the path that will lead to the next village. She walks proudly with her head held high as the **villagers** and her family wave goodbye.

● **Narrator:** The very next morning, Maiba sets off on her journey. She is confident that it won't be long until she is the wife of the Great Chief.

● **Villagers:** Good luck, Maiba, travel safely!

*A little while later, **Maiba** spots a **mouse** at the edge of the road.*

● **Mouse:** *(looking up at **Maiba**)* Do you need me to show you the way to the village?

*Maiba waves her hand dismissively at the little **mouse**.*

● **Maiba:** I do not need your help. Now *(shouting)* GO!

● **Mouse:** *(warningly)* If you are unkind to all those that try to help you, you will fail.

● **Maiba:** You are not worthy to speak to me. I shall soon be the wife of the Great Chief. Leave me alone.

*The **mouse** runs away in fright.*

● **Narrator:** Maiba continues to travel on once more and before long she sees a frog in the middle of the path.

*Enter the **frog**.*

● **Frog:** Shall I show you the way to the next village? For it is hard to find with all the twists and turns in this path.

● **Maiba:** *(angrily)* Get away from me you slimy frog! How dare you speak to ME!

*Maiba runs past the **frog**, looking at him in disgust.*

● **Narrator:** Once more Maiba journeys onwards. When she stops to eat some bread, she meets an old begging woman sitting at the edge of the road.

● **Old woman:** *(holding out her hand to **Maiba**)* Might you have a spare crumb of bread to feed a hungry old woman?

● **Maiba:** *(knocking the **old woman**'s hand away)* No, I do not, you flithy old woman. Get away from me.

● **Old woman:** *(speaking gently)* Listen carefully, child. You must not always be so cruel for misfortune awaits you. You will soon see some trees that will laugh at you but you must not laugh in return. You will see a jug of milk but you must not drink from it.

● **Maiba:** I won't listen to you. I do not need advice from an ugly, old woman! Now, go away!

● **Old woman:** You have been warned…

SCENE 3

CHARACTERS IN THIS SCENE:

● **Narrator** ● **Maiba** ● **A young girl** ● **Extras –**
A chorus of trees, washer-women and villagers

*Maiba reaches the forest and sees the river.
The afternoon sun is beginning to set over the
glistening water.*

● **Narrator:** Before long, Maiba reaches a forest
of trees. Just as the old woman had warned, the trees
begin to laugh at her.

● **Chorus of trees:** Ha, ha, ha, ha, ha!

● **Maiba:** (*laughing back at the trees*) Ha, ha, ha! Oh, how funny!
Laughing trees, whoever saw such a thing before!

● **Narrator:** But Maiba quickly thinks no more of the trees when
she spots a jug of milk beside a tree trunk. She is thirsty from
her long journey and drinks it all in one go. As Maiba wipes her
mouth, she sees a group of washer-women at the edge of the
river. One young girl looks up and waves to Maiba.

● **Young girl:** Where are you going, Sister? Might we help and show you the way to your destination?

● **Washer-women:** Yes, we would be pleased to help you, Child. Where do you travel to?

● **Maiba:** *(speaking angrily)* Stop asking me questions! How dare you call me your sister and child. You are nothing to me. I will soon be the wife of a Great Chief.

*Maiba crosses the river away from the **washer-women** and they watch sadly as she walks away without looking back.*

● **Narrator:** Eventually, Maiba reaches the Great Chief's village. She speaks to the villagers and tells them that she has come to meet their chief.

*Maiba enters the village as the **villagers** come to greet her.*

● **A villager:** You must be careful, for the chief is a clever man. He will not want a foolish wife. We suggest you make him a meal ready for his return at sunset.

*The **villagers** show **Maiba** into the **Great Chief**'s hut.*

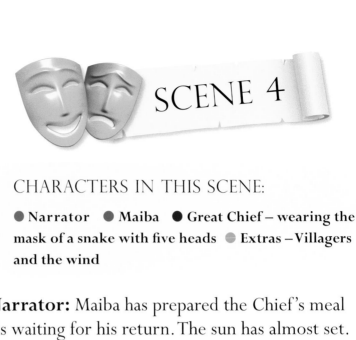

SCENE 4

CHARACTERS IN THIS SCENE:

● **Narrator** ● **Maiba** ● **Great Chief** – wearing the mask of a snake with five heads ● **Extras** – Villagers and the wind

●**Narrator:** Maiba has prepared the Chief's meal and is waiting for his return. The sun has almost set.

●**Maiba:** (*talking to herself*) It's getting late. I have ground the grain and made the bread but where is the Great Chief?

●**Narrator:** Just then a strong wind starts to blow.

●**The wind:** Wooo, woooo, wooo, WOOOO!

●**Narrator:** The Great Chief enters his hut. He is a man with the heads of five snakes. Ten pairs of snake eyes glare angrily back at Maiba.

● **Maiba:** (*screaming in fright, covers her eyes*)
You hideous creature! What are you?

● **Great Chief:** (*gravely*) I am the Great Chief
but you will **never** be my wife. I know that you have
been cruel, proud and unkind to those that have tried to
help you. I will have no wife who behaves in such a way.
Return to your village at once!

*And, with that, **Maiba** flees the villlage in fear.*

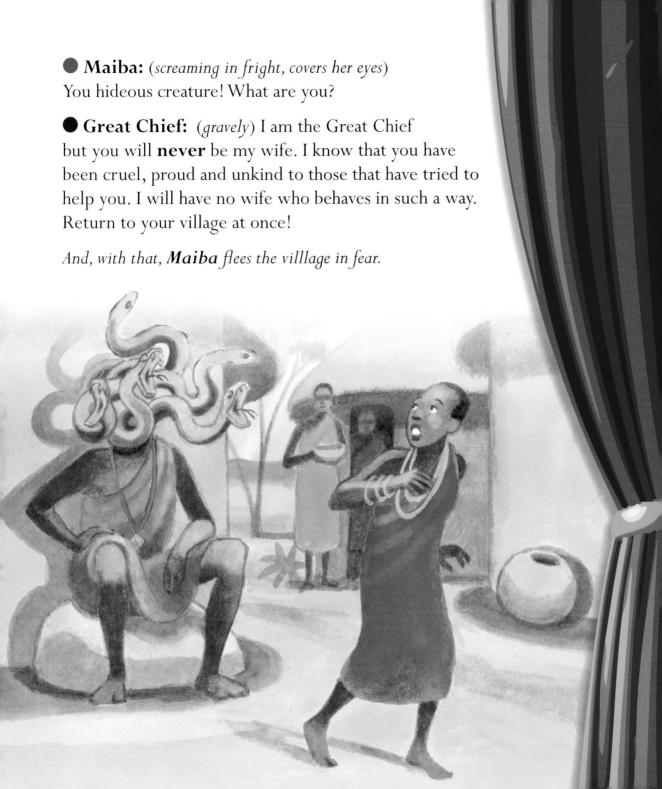

SCENE 5

CHARACTERS IN THIS SCENE:

- **Narrator** ● **Sundai** ● **Rufaro** ● **Maiba**
- **Daya** ● **Extras – The villagers**

Sundai, Rufaro and Daya are in the hut, listening to Maiba's telling of what has come to pass. She is weeping as she tells her father all that has happened.

● **Narrator:** Upon Maiba's return her father is very disappointed. He worries that his daughter has upset the Great Chief and ruined the family's chances of being linked to such an important village. Daya, upon seeing her father's distress, is keen to make her father happy once again.

Daya: Father, may I go to the village and try to please the Great Chief?

Rufaro: *(looking anxiously between **Sundai** and **Daya**)* Are you sure, Daya? Sundai, we have surely upset the Chief greatly. Might it be wise to leave the Great Chief alone and not anger him further?

Maiba: *(suddenly cries out)* The Great Chief is a hateful, ugly creature. You'll not want him as a husband, believe me!

Villagers: *(laughing as one **villager** speaks to the rest)* He, he, he! It sounds like the Great Chief showed her what kind of wife he doesn't want! Daya will be much better suited.

● **Sundai:** *(smiling at **Daya**)* I do not fear the Great Chief's anger, for he is a fair and decent man, kind to his village and to all those he meets. In return, Daya is a sweet girl, Rufaro. I truly believe she'll make the Great Chief a wonderful wife.

● **Daya:** *(standing and kissing **Sundai**'s cheek)* Thank you, Father. Please will you gather a bridal party for me, for I wish to show the Chief how proud I am of the village I come from.

● **Rufaro:** Yes, Sundai, we must do it right this time.

● **Sundai:** I agree. I will gather a party immediately, for no time must be lost.

*Sundai steps out into the village square and addresses the **villagers**.*

● **Sundai:** Everyone, listen to me. I need to send my daughter to the Great Chief with the best bridal party he has ever seen. Who will help me?

● **Villagers:** We will help! We will help!

*Very soon a large crowd of **villagers** has gathered to travel with **Daya** to meet the **Great Chief**.*

SCENE 6

CHARACTERS IN THIS SCENE:

- **Narrator** • **An old woman** • **A mouse** • **A frog**
- **Daya** • **A young girl** • **Extras – The bridal party**

Daya *is travelling along the path to the next village with her large* **bridal party**.

● **Narrator:** Daya sets off to meet the Great Chief. As her sister before her, Daya meets the mouse.

● **Mouse:** Can I help you find your way to the village?

○ **Daya:** *(smiles kindly and bends down to speak to the mouse)* Yes please, for I am sure to lose my way.

● **Mouse:** You must follow the road you are travelling on until you reach a large stone. From there, take the left path.

● **Narrator:** Daya thanks the mouse and follows the path he has shown her.

*She soon meets the same **frog** her sister met, sitting in the middle of the path, waiting for her. **Daya** gently picks up the frog.*

● **Frog:** Can I show you the way to the next village? For there are many twists and turns in this path.

● **Daya:** Thank you. I would be most grateful for your help. It is getting late and I wish to reach the village before sunset.

● **Frog:** The quickest way is through the trees up ahead. Once you see the river, the village is on the other side.

● **Daya:** You are very kind. Thank you.

***Daya** puts the **frog** back down and continues on her way.*

Daya *continues along the path and soon sees a row of trees in the distance.*

Narrator: At the edge of the forest, Daya meets an old beggar woman. Daya gives the frail woman her last loaf of bread. *(Hands over a loaf of bread.)*

Old woman: Thank you for your kindness, Child. In return I shall offer you some advice. When you see a young girl by the river, take care to speak to her kindly.

Bridal party: Come along Daya, we must hurry. We must reach the village by nightfall.

Daya: *(turning to the **bridal party**)* Just a moment, please. *(to the **old woman**)* Thank you for your advice. I will do all that you advise.

Sure enough, **Daya** *soon sees the* **young girl** *by the water's edge.*

Young girl: Where are you going to, Sister?

Daya: *(smiling)* My journey has reached its end. I am here to see the Great Chief in the village just across this river.

Young Girl: *(looks at **Daya** gravely)* When you meet him will you be afraid and look away from his face?

Bridal party: (*scoffing*) Daya is too good and kind to be afraid of anyone's appearance.

Daya: (*steadily returns the **young girl**'s gaze*) I promise I will look him directly in the eyes.

Young Girl: I believe you. (*gives **Daya** some bread and meat from her basket*) Now take this food and prepare a meal for the Great Chief's return this evening. His hut is just across the river. Go now and get ready.

SCENE 7

CHARACTERS IN THIS SCENE:

- **Narrator** ● **Daya** ● **Great Chief**
- **Extras – Villagers and the wind**

● **Narrator:** Daya prepares and cooks a meal while she waits for the Great Chief. A strong wind can soon be heard and the Great Chief, masked as a five-headed snake, enters the hut.

● **The wind:** Wooo, woooo, woooo, WOOOOO!

Daya looks at the Great Chief.

● **Narrator:** Bravely, Daya looks at the Chief's five snake heads and into his many piercing yellow eyes. She is afraid but is determined to keep her promise to the young girl at the river and will not look away in fear.

● **Daya:** Good evening, Chief. I have prepared your evening meal. I hope you enjoy it for I have worked hard all evening.

*The **Great Chief** sits down to eat his meal. Pause whilst he eats.*

● **Great Chief:** (*smiling at* **Daya**) Your food is delicious, Daya, thank you. More importantly, I know you are a kind and caring girl.

● **Daya:** (*looks him directly in the eyes*) May I ask, how could you know that?

● **Great Chief:** It was I who was the mouse, the frog and the old woman. I was even the young girl washing clothes in the river. I have seen how kind and generous you are. Please say you will be my wife?

The **Great Chief** *removes his mask and reveals the true man he is.*

● **Daya:** (*smiling*) I will, for I know we will be very happy.

● **Villagers:** (*cheering and clapping*) The Chief has found a wife!

● **Narrator:** And Daya was right. With each year that passed, the Great Chief loved his wife all the more. In return, Daya was the best wife she could be. But more importantly she remained as kind and true to all those she met as the day she left her home to become the Chief's bride.

The End

There are lots of websites you can visit to find out about Africa. Here are a few good places to begin:

CBBC: http://news.bbc.co.uk/cbbcnews/hi/static/find_out/specials/newsround_extra/africa/html/default.stm
Find out all about Africa, its people and its cultures.

More African Tales: http://africa.mrdonn.org/fables.html
If you enjoyed reading this folktale, find more on this website.

First published in 2011 by Wayland

Copyright © Wayland 2011

Wayland
338 Euston Road
London
NW1 3BH

Wayland Australia
Level 17/207 Kent Street
Sydney NSW 2000

All rights reserved.

Editor: Katie Woolley
Designer: Elaine Wilkinson
Illustrator: Adrienne Kennaway

British Library Cataloguing in Publication Data

Powell, Jenny.
An African tale. -- (Putting on a play)
1. Africa--Juvenile drama.
I. Title II. Series
822.9'2-dc22

ISBN: 978 0 7502 6551 5

Printed in China

Wayland is a division of Hachette Children's Books, an Hachette UK company.
www.hachette.co.uk